Kiss
Your
Brain

Kiss Your Brain

Volume I:
Diagnosis Diaries

Christina Costa

First edition: February 2021

IBSN: 978-1-7366434-2-6 (paperback)

Kiss Your Brain, Volume I: Diagnosis Diaries
Christina Costa

If you are interested in bulk ordering copies of this text, please contact the author:
naegeli@umich.edu

*To brave brain tumor
patients and their caregivers*

Contents

Introduction

Thank you for selecting this collection of poems. I have always journaled and written poems therapeutically. After taking a poetry class in college, I started to do so even more regularly. The first I wrote during this experience, which is included in this collection, was written while I was in the emergency room when the tumor was found. I wrote three more that night when I couldn't sleep.

The themes of these poems are inspired by my time as a teacher. When I was a middle school science teacher, at the end of the day, I would tell my students to "kiss their brain" for all the beautiful work that it does after seeing a kindergarten teacher colleague do the same. They would send a little kiss and tap it on their head as a routine and mantra for all the wonderful things we did during the day.

This phrase continued to be a central theme in my life. As a neurodivergent educator, I am always

learning how to challenge power, privilege, and advo-
cate for my mental health. Then, when my life was
turned around with a brain tumor diagnosis, I
couldn't help but think of kissing my brain and loving
it throughout the process.

My Story

I started getting migraines when I was twenty-six. My father and sister had always had them, so it didn't mean much to me . . . just that it was "my time." I remember asking others for advice on managing those migraines. I tried everything. I thought migraines were just going to be a part of my life.

Then my migraines started getting weird. I was a Ph.D. student at the time, and I was on campus, working. As usual, my migraines began with a small blurry spot in my left visual field, and then this blur got bigger and bigger until I couldn't see anything. Then this time, the left side of my face went numb, along with my left arm. I walked to the campus health center (probably quite crookedly on account of my entire visual field being blurred). I checked in to the walk-in clinic and explained my symptoms. I saw the physician and was promptly sent home with the advice to get Tylenol.

My migraines continued, and later that year, they started getting worse. I scheduled an appointment with another doctor. This time they prescribed me a type of migraine medicine and warned me that they might make my symptoms "better or worse," which was great. If you guessed worse, you're right. I threw out the medicine and took the doctor up on their offer to refer me to a neurologist. The first appointment they had was seven months away. I booked it and went back to my monthly migraines.

A couple of months later is when things started getting weird. I would get acid reflux at night and felt numbness in my left hand often. I called the neurologist's office again and asked if there were any cancellations—there weren't.

Then, I got the final symptom that started to worry me. I would get "dizzy spells" (what we would later find out were focal seizures) throughout the day. I would feel dizzy as if I were about to faint, and then I would go to the ground and put my head to the floor. When they would come to an end, I would feel acid in my throat. I had no idea why this was happening. For a short while, I thought I could even be pregnant. These would occur when I was going for walks, writing on my computer for too long, or in the middle of the night.

I had been dismissed so many times before that it probably took me a month of having seizures before I called the neurologist's office again. Every time I had a seizure, I would stay in that position and just pray that something wasn't wrong. I honestly didn't think of what could be happening. I called the neurologist's office three more times and finally got in for a video visit after explaining my symptoms.

I talked to the doctor. He completed a Neuro evaluation, told me all the things doctors had told me before about migraines, and then asked if I ever had any imaging done. I said no, and he ordered an MRI, which I then scheduled for the first available appointment later in the month.

I was not worried on the day of the MRI. It was raining hard that day, I almost didn't go, but then I thought it would be cool to have some images of my brain to show my students when I taught brain imaging in Intro Psych. It turns out, the desire for some cool PowerPoint slides was much more compelling than the dizzy spells. I got the MRI, probably went to Target, and then back home that Sunday afternoon to get ready for the week.

My husband and I were watching Netflix and about to go to bed. I got a phone call at about 10:30 p.m. I didn't answer because I thought it was weird, and then I realized it was the hospital's area code and thought I should listen to the voice mail. That's when we heard the unimaginable.

I couldn't believe my ears as the doctor said to get to an emergency room and page him. I fell to the floor. My husband got me back up, and we called the doctor. "There is a large mass in the right hemisphere of your brain." We called my parents, packed a small bag, and got ready to leave.

On the way out, I went to the bathroom and started crying as I looked at the mirror. I have always had a habit of writing my goals on sticky notes and posting them to the mirror. I had taken a pregnancy test and a red Sharpie and filled it in to look positive. I posted that test to the mirror as a reminder and hoped that one day it would be the result of a test I would take.

I cried, not at the loss of another month not being pregnant, but the thought that my body is so smart that it knew it wasn't the right time for me. My body had been telling me the entire year.

The ER

We got in the car and drove to the emergency room. I will never forget how calm my husband was. He was my rock on the night my world turned upside down. In the time of Corona Virus (COVID-19), no one was allowed in the emergency room with me. My husband dropped me off, and my parents (who were on their way) arranged to find a spot to meet him when they got there. I walked calmly into one of the scariest places in the world and checked in.

"We were expecting you," the check-in person said. "Great," I said. I sat down and waited—alone with my thoughts. I looked down at my wrist. "Still I Rise" is tattooed on my left wrist. I got the tattoo after I finished my first year of teaching. I thought nothing could be more challenging than my first year of teaching (haha!). I think about Maya Angelou's "Still I Rise" often. While I had become so removed from the hardships of being a first-year teacher, it still reminded me of my students because we studied her work together. There, in the ER waiting room, it gave me an enormous rush to be thinking of them.

I was called back into the ER, hooked up to all the cords and monitors, and a PA came to tell me the news. This was the start of a fun new game that I call "how will they break the news"—and this game continued for every person who walked into my room in the next twenty-four hours. I had no idea how much they knew, and so it was as if everyone coming in (and there were many—PAs, nurses, residents, fellows, etc.) was explaining to me what was going on inside my head for the first time.

The PA pulled up my MRI and showed me the mass in my brain. I called my mom, dad, and husband to be on the phone, as she explained. It was . . . big. My mom asked if I would send her a picture, and I remember saying, "Are you sure you want to see it? It's big."

Then I started laughing. The PA looked at me, confused, and I just told her, "I just know way too much about this." We laughed together, and soon I was admitted to neurosurgery. I still had no idea what this was or how urgent it was. The doctors ordered a chest and pelvic CT to check the rest of my body, and I was moved to another floor.

By this time, it was about midnight. I started calling people and sent some messages to close friends and family. I even recorded some videos (which are great to look back on—highly recommend). Early that morning, I was admitted to the neuro floor, and I spent the day meeting and talking to new nurses and residents. Then at the end of the day, I met my assigned neurosurgeon for the first time.

He came in, pulled up my MRI, and explained what the tumor most likely was and the plan. The first step in these types of tumors is planning for surgery to remove as much as possible.

Surgery would be soon but not that week. We scheduled to meet in the neurosurgery clinic later the next week, scheduled an fMRI, and I was discharged from the hospital with antiseizure meds and a fear that I'd never felt before. Even though I was scared, I felt safe (something I would say over and over). It was the medical professionals who made me feel that way. And I will always be thankful for them.

Surgery

The month leading up to surgery went fast and slow at the same time. When doctors referred to my tumor, they always said, "most likely a glioma," and that entire month, I didn't dare Google what a glioma was. My fear was confirmed when someone sent me a blog-like article on a woman who had a brain tumor, and she said something along the lines of "Doctors thought it was a glioma, but *thank God*, it was not . . . Never Google the term glioma." I read that post and cried for a few days, then focused back on the upcoming surgery.

My suspicions were further questioned when we met with a team at the hospital, and one of the team members was a neuro-oncologist. I am not sure what I thought the large tumor in my brain was, but I didn't even imagine the possibilities at that time.

In the ER, I remember talking to a nurse and saying, "OMG, I am going to have to be awake during surgery, aren't I?" and he said, "You have been watching too much *Grey's Anatomy*, haven't you?" I followed up with, "Yeah . . . but tell me right now, am I going to have to be awake or not?" An awake craniotomy was set.

I asked my doctor what it would feel like, and he assured me that I wouldn't feel any pain but that I might remember some pieces, and I would be tested during the awake portion. I didn't overthink it, and mostly the days leading up to surgery were filled with adrenaline, reading, and lots of watching *The Office*.

The night before surgery, my neurosurgeon called and asked if I was ready. "I'm ready," I said, "are you?" He confirmed he was ready too. In hindsight, I don't know how I had the guts to ask a neurosurgeon if they were ready, but I hope he knows I wasn't questioning him (lol). It was one of the most human things. Hearing from him and spending the night with my family, I slept well and woke up ready.

We went to the hospital, went to pre-op, met all the wonderful people who were going to be in that room, and then my mom finally left to go to surgery waiting, and I was wheeled back to the operating room. I remember them doing the safety check, everyone introducing themselves, and then the anesthesiologist asking if I was ready. I do remember waking up, but I remember very few details. I remember being cold and a nurse giving me a blanket. I remember a nurse putting a wet sponge in my mouth to keep me hydrated. I remember answering some questions and feeling a cold sensation in my head, but that was it.

The next thing I remember is waking up in the post-op area. I remember seeing my nurses and my mom. I remember seeing my surgeon. I don't think I said anything, but I remember wanting and trying to say "thank you, thank you, thank you."

ICU

I spent four days in the ICU and two days on the Neuro floor. Those days were filled with the kindest people in the world and one visitor per day per COVID guidelines. I remember wiggling my toes and fingers and thinking of how wild it was that I could do that. I recorded more videos on my phone, which would later prove to be hilarious. I went live on Instagram while I had my breakfast in the ICU the day after surgery (My apologies to whoever attended that live because who knows what I said).

Those days were mostly comprised of sleeping, and neuro checks ("Tap your finger to your nose." "What day is it?" "Where are you?"; "Repeat this sentence after me . . ."; "Squeeze my fingers"; "Wiggle your toes"; "Okay, I'm going to shine this light in your eyes . . .").

I also got a post-surgery MRI. The results were incredible and far beyond what we were expecting. It was so cool to see the before and after, and I continued to be so grateful for my medical team and so proud of what my brain had gone through. I walked for the first time in the hospital, was able to start eating, called many friends and family, enjoyed my daily visitors, and was discharged to go home exactly a week post-surgery.

13

What's Next

At first, going home felt weird. I learned to trust my body again, and it was hard not to be at the hospital where I was 100 percent safe. My mom helped me shower, my dad made me breakfast, my husband helped me start to walk again, and my dog cuddled with me while I fell in and out of sleep all day.

The post-surgery pain was a lot to manage. I learned tips and tricks from others. I got lots of headache wraps (Amazon and Etsy), large sunglasses that fit my swollen head to block out light that bothered me, and propped up an enormous number of pillows to be able to get as much sleep as I could. When I would wake up in the night and could not sleep, I made a little song and would say over and over, "I am healthy, I am well, I feel good, I feel swell" (pretty sure it was the first time I'd ever said "swell" in my life).

Then after a few weeks, the appointments started to ramp up again. I had an appointment to go over pathology reports and get my staples removed. When pathology came back after surgery, chemotherapy and radiation therapy treatments were planned; I was diagnosed with anaplastic astrocytoma (grade 3, IDH mutant).

Sharing those pathology reports with the world and the upcoming treatment plan would lead me to the most challenging time since diagnosis. After thinking about why it was so difficult to comprehend, I started to understand.

I was immediately met with the message of being able to fight. I rejected that narrative. I didn't want to fight my tumor. I didn't want to fight my brain. I loved my brain for all that it was, is, and will be. I kissed my brain every single day and loved my body, even while fighting the unimaginable.

I started to ignore those messages. I planned for fertility preservation and had another set of wonderful doctors and health care professionals who helped me preserve my eggs. I met with the new members of my team and learned about the plan for chemo and radiation. I got more MRIs, was fitted for my radiation mask, and had an education session at the cancer center about the chemo I was going to take.

The first phase of my treatment was radiation appointments (Monday-Friday) and chemo every day. As I am writing this, I am on the last week of this treatment. The next steps are twelve more chemo rounds, with lots of blood testing and, you guessed it, MRIs.

This Collection

All these poems were written throughout this period of my life: from the day I found out I had a brain tumor to my awake craniotomy, surgery recovery, going through fertility preservation, and my first phase of chemo and radiation treatment.

They are real and raw. I did not organize them by order, rather by theme. It is interesting to read them back because some of them remain so salient—I can remember the exact place and feelings I had when I wrote them. On the other hand, there are poems that I can barely remember writing, but I didn't remove any because I wanted to document and remember this whole experience, for the good times and hard times.

I hope you can interpret them in ways that are helpful for you. I hope these poems can bring comfort and healing to other teachers, students, neurodivergent individuals, brain tumor patients, and caregivers.

V1

Thank You, Reader

Through purchasing this book, you have donated to research on advancing our knowledge and medicine of brain tumors and brain cancer. I thank you from the bottom of my brain for supporting this cause. I have so much hope for brain tumor patients and brain tumor medicine.

We need more awareness and more research. I hope I can use my voice and my story to share my experiences with you and raise money for this research.

Thank you,
Christina

V1

I. On Beautiful Brains

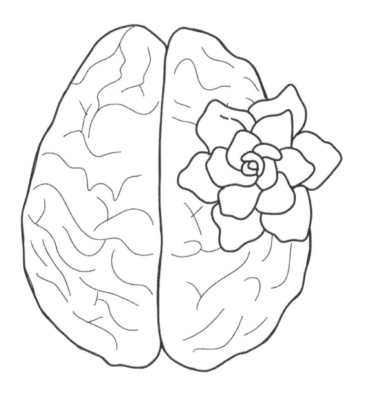

Kiss Your Brain

How many times a day
do we thank our bodies
for what they do?

They are
our sanctuaries

Kiss your
big
beautiful
brain

Thank
your
whole
body
ceaselessly

My Prayer

Give me
the strength
to carry this

Give me
the strength
to survive
this

then, (please)

Give me
the strength
to show the others
that
they can
survive it
too

My Brain

She is beautiful
She is powerful
She is intelligent

She has a trespasser
That is not welcome
That came without permission
just like so many other things
we don't expect in life

But she is brave
and even though she is scared-
she will face the unexpected

She is resilient

Unconditional Love

& even after all
we've been through
After something awful
invaded you

You let me smell
You let me think
You let me process
You let me laugh
You love me

~unconditionally~

and I'll love you, brain,

For the rest
of my life

Teacher with a Tumor

I teach about the mind
and the whole time
there was
something in mine

But I still love her
for all she does
I think I love
her
   even
      more

How is it possible
to love something
that is trying
to destroy you?

...

Acceptance
& hope
& resilience
& peace

The Fire

They say
"you're so strong"

But what they
don't know is:
When your world is on fire,
you have no choice
but to become

the flame

Pleasant Patient

"The patient, Christina, presents for the evaluation of a large right insular brain tumor"

"She is a very pleasant, 27-year-old, Ph.D. student"

A stream of consciousness hits me as I read my after-patient care summary and see hints of humanity amongst my diagnosis. It makes me feel like a person. Ever since seeing the image, I could only picture myself with the mass. The intruder. Something that didn't "belong." But now I see that they see me for a person too. They can see that I am ready to face it with strength. That I will be in the operating room with them too. They are not alone. Neither am I. I am not just a brain tumor patient. I am pleasant. I am a student. I am a teacher. I am a woman.

I am here.

I Love You

I love you,
brain
You did nothing wrong
My love
for you
is unequivocal

What if we
started
loving
the parts of our bodies
that are hurting?

Nothing
ever
healed well
with
hate anyway

Women in Medicine

The doctor came to visit
before surgery
"I'm the anesthesiology
resident,"
she said

My mother looked at her
"Will you hold my baby's hand
when they wake her up?"

She asked me for consent
"Can I hold your hand?"
I said yes

I'm still positive
that I wouldn't
have survived
a brain surgery
without
her
hand

Criminal

I paid $372.54 at CVS
for a medication
that keeps me alive

Health care is criminal
~I thought~
as I swiped my card

"You said that out loud,"
the cashier said

No . . .
I didn't say it
loud (or soon) enough

You Should Name Your Tumor

I thought about naming it—
the disease

Something ugly
Horrible
Something you could
shout (angrily)
with spite

But I can't hate something
that is a part of me
that's seen me cry
that's seen me dance
that's seen me love
that's seen me fall
on my hands and knees

I think
I'll name it
f a i t h

Law of Attraction

It's
nothing
that
you
did

-The doctor said-

I hope
everyone
can hear that

You
did
not
manifest
your
trauma

Ruminating

What if,
what if,
what if?

A million scenarios
race through my mind

-But-

What if it
all works out?

Community Healing

I don't know
what it's like
to hit the ground

Because
there has always
been someone there
to soften the blow

How can I
soften the blow
for the people
who helped
me rise
when I fell?

Generalized Anxiety

Hard to describe . . .

Feels like
    heart racing
    stomach dropping

Sounds like
    people saying
    "meditate"
    "relax"
    "don't worry"

Tastes like
    antidepressants
    and stigma

No threats in sight,
but the body reacts to them

Anxiety will always
be a part of me

But just as
I learn to
live with it

I live to
learn with it

It makes me better

My mind is different,
but it is strong

What You Can See

I am neurodivergent in a couple of
ways
    Brain Tumor
    Generalized Anxiety
    Seizure Disorder

But only one of those diagnoses
came with something tangible
that people can *see*

I carry the weight
of these diversities
having different tangibility

I see the privilege
granted to those with
"something to fix"
& the powerlessness and stigma
attached with the ones
that are diagnosed
by a manual

They are all serious
I want them all to be seen
They are all part of me

Mental health is real

Mental health is important

Mental health exists
in countless realities

Post-Traumatic Growth

These
memories
stick
to me
like glue

I remember
    the phone call
I remember
    falling to the floor
I remember
    seeing the picture
I remember
    calling my loved ones
I remember
    rolling back to the OR
I remember
    waking up during surgery
I remember
    the second MRI
I remember
    the panic that hit again
I will always remember
    the way people looked at me

christina costa

This is a new part of me
I am learning to live
with survivor stress

I will not fall,
but I will
thrive
because of it

Teaching Mental Health

I prioritize my students'
mental health
Just like they have sick days
when they have the flu,
they have mental health days
to take care of their
beautiful brains

I've learned that
I set the example
for what that means

Saying "mental health"
isn't enough
I need to role model
my own mental health
and show them
what it means
to thrive in a world
that prioritizes productivity
and ableism

I hope to teach them
about their brains
but also, how to take
care of themselves

We do it together
as a community
and as a classroom

V1

I will keep ~~fighting~~ living
I will keep ~~fighting~~ loving
I will keep ~~fighting~~ living

I will keep ~~fighting~~ living
I will keep ~~fighting~~ loving
I will keep ~~fighting~~ living

I will keep ~~fighting~~ living
I will keep ~~fighting~~ loving
I will keep ~~fighting~~ living

I will keep ~~fighting~~ living
I will keep ~~fighting~~ loving
I will keep ~~fighting~~ living

I will keep ~~fighting~~ living
I will keep ~~fighting~~ loving
I will keep ~~fighting~~ living

I will keep ~~fighting~~ living
I will keep ~~fighting~~ loving
I will keep ~~fighting~~ living

My Story

This isn't the story
I originally wrote,
but it is mine

The story I wrote
had a small house
in a "cool" neighborhood
A front porch
and a French-pressed coffee

The story I wrote
had less pain
less suffering
fewer medical bills

The story I wrote
had a baby on the way
a summer trip to the beach
and Sunday brunch at twelve

The story I wrote isn't mine
and I'm not sure who
I thought I was
to be writing
my own story
in the first place

My new story hurts

I feel it
Every waking second

It smells like a hospital
looks like a sea of a
community's tears
feels like the weight
of a grand piano

The story that
was written for me
burns in my chest

But I know
-I believe-
this story was written
just for me

This new story
is mine

Fighter

I tried it on
to see how it felt
Because I kept hearing
those words
next to name
    like a job
    like an identity
    like a role

~Fighter~

I look at myself
in the mirror
it felt okay
—at first

But soon it became
exhausting
Too heavy to lift
Too much to carry
Too burdensome to bear

I took it off
and left it on the floor
war was not for me
a body is not
a battlefield

Heroes Work Here

You never forget
the voice mail that says
"come in right now"

You also never forget
the person who shows you
the scan

Or, most importantly,
the person who says
"This is what I do"

I prayed for my
Guardian Angel
to show me themselves
in the physical world

Seconds later,
A family member
showed me a picture
of my doctor

My angel
gave me
the confidence
I needed
to survive

Community

When I think of
the people
who are lifting me up

I can feel them
Hear them
See them

I wonder if they
will ever understand

That
they
healed me

That
they
saved me

And here I thought
I was teaching them

Community matters
and *nothing*
else
does

My Visualization

My tumor is a pile of dirt that needs to be removed. I see a shovel and the pile next to it. I take time thinking of different students I have taught over the past five years. Every time I visualize, different students come to mind. They take the shovel and start digging. I think of everything they have taught me and how much I have grown as a person because of them. I see different students come and take turns shoveling until there is only a small pile left. Then, I see my family and my doctors come to the pile. They sweep up the remaining dirt until there is only an empty hole left. Next, my future children approach the hole (fun fact, they always appear as twins). They are smiling, laughing, and they have my husband's hair and my dimples. With the help of their dad, they take a big beautiful plant and place it in the hole. Most days I fall asleep right after I see the plant blooming and my family smiling at me.

I end up feeling so grateful every time. Savoring the memories I've created with my family and students and all the wonderful memories that will still be created.

Slow Progress Is Progress

A week ago,
I couldn't
read a sentence

Today,
I read
a book

Listen to your body
It knows how to heal

That's its job

And your job
is to trust it

Notes on My Phone

"I believe in
miracles"

"Angels
watch
over me"

"Do it for
the others"

Loving > Fighting

I am not
   at war
      with my body

The opposite

I love my body
I love it no matter what
I love it for the things
it can do
   and can't

"You're young and healthy"
"Your body will make
connections again"

But what if it doesn't?

My body is
worthy of loving

No matter
        what connections it makes
No matter
        how long it takes me to move
                to write
                to feel
                to think

I love my body
It did not betray me
It was given
different instructions
And I will live and love
those instructions

  No more wars
   No battles
     No fighting

I will love it—
through the good
and the bad

-No exceptions-

Health Care Heroes

Some people are
given a gift

They make you feel
    Comfortable
    Peaceful
    Hopeful

Just by walking
in the room

I am forever
in debt
to the people
that made me
feel safe
when everything else
told me not to

Storm Approaching

My body
is the water

Waves run
through me
like a storm

And every time
the ocean crashes
I find a way
to move with
the turbulence

This is resilience

Your body
is made of water
too

What Tragedy Can Do
Inspired by "What Cancer Cannot Do"

Tragedy can kick you down
and lift you up
in the same breath

It can make friendships stronger
It can give you purpose
It can inspire
It can breed hope
It can strengthen faith
It can accelerate dreams

It can bring an
unexplainable peace
A love for your body
that you never knew

It can introduce you
to the bravest people
that walk this earth
and the smartest people
born to help you heal

And that's why
I'm not scared

Thank you, tragedy
For what you've taught me
it's now time
for you
to go

Identity First Language

I am not
a patient
with a brain tumor

I am
a neurodivergent
patient

I am not
a person
with a disability

I am
a disabled
person

I am not
a woman with
a chronic illness

I am
a chronically ill
woman

When will
they realize
my identities
are me

My Why

I found this letter in my notebook
from the day I left middle school
teaching to go to graduate school:

Dear Students,

Hi. I love you . . . you know that
already.

You have no idea what you did for
me and what you have given me. It's
not really fair because I just
taught you about layers of the
earth and photosynthesis, but you
taught me about life.

You taught me how to be a resilient
person. You taught me that no matter what is happening that I need
to get up and be there for you and
I tried every day to be. I know I
made mistakes so thank you for let-
ting me make those. I'm not perfect
but there wasn't one day I wasn't
ready to teach you.

Since I met you, I've thought about
nothing except you. I will think
about you for the rest of my life.
Believe it or not you will probably
forget about me, but I hope you
will remember the wild teacher that
danced and laughed and exaggerated
about how cool the rock cycle actually is. I will remember you in my
research, I will remember you when
I feel hopeful, and I will cer-
tainly remember you when I have
children of my own. I hope they are
like you.

I will be teaching college when you
are first year college students.
One day, other students in the
class will say, "What is she doing?" and you will be there to
whisper back, "That's just Dr.
Costa . . . get used to it." Thanks
for making me the woman I am today.
I love you. I rise because of you.

Love,
Ms. Costa

Letting Go of Fear

A statistic
showed me
how many years
I had left

I cried for
two weeks

  Night
   and
    Day

I stopped dreaming
and then

...

...

...

I stopped
relying on
numbers that
didn't recognize
me as an individual

Radiation

I cried the entire
appointment
Just wishing
someone would tell me
that I was going
to be ok

He looked at me
and he did not
tell me that
-But-
What he did say to me
was more powerful
than a million suns

"You are living the impossible
and you are doing it"

Those words
radiate through my body

Throughout my journey,
they will never go away,
and for that
I am grateful

V1

III. On Renewal

Renewal

Resilience is not
putting on a
smile
while the world
explodes

Resilience is scary
Resilience is hard
Resilience is taxing

Resilience is waking up
each day
despite not knowing
what it will bring
and living it
anyway

Survivor

You
earn
the
title
~Survivor~
the
day
you
hear
your
diagnosis

Dear Trauma

At first, that day
haunted me
gave me
nightmares

But over time,
I saw how strong
it made me

So, I wrote a letter
to the *me* that
survived that day

Dear Surgery Day Me,

You are so brave. You are a miracle. I am so proud of what you did.
This won't be easy, but one day you
will understand. One day you will
use this day to help others.

You don't have to feel strong right
now, but because of your existence,
you will give others a chance. The
love I have for you is endless.

If I could go back and warn you, I
wouldn't—because this journey is
ours, and I can't wait for you to
see what we do.

I love you.

Write a letter
to the *you*
who survived

Productive

Relax

My body screamed
    for a break
    for a second to breath
    for a moment to renew

I didn't listen
...
until I had to

Now I measure
productivity
in other ways

Minutes of peace
    of time together
    of travel
    of writing
    of feeling

Listen to your body
It is telling you
what it needs

And we have
been taught
how to mute

It's time
to turn up
the volume

Neurodivergent

Neuro = related to the
nervous system

Divergent = tending to
be different;
straying from the
"norm"

Neurodivergent =
Super cool
human with
superpowers

Celebrate Neurodiversity

How cool it is
to see the world
feel the world
experience the world
in a different way

Rise

One day
Some day
I'll get back
up again

Because that's
what I was
taught
to do

We rise

Waking Up

Every
 day
  that
   you
    wake
    up
   is
  a
miracle

christina costa

don't ever believe
anything else

Waiting Rooms

In this world,
there are
the scariest
of rooms
that you
never dream
you will
find yourself

But I promise
you this

In those rooms are
the bravest
people you will
ever get the chance
to meet

You don't have
to be scared

They will lift you
In faith
In hope
In confidence
In inspiration

Hope

There is always hope
Say those words
again
  and
    again

One day,
hope
will
become
habit

Gratitude

How do you
thank
the people that
saved your
life

It might be impossible
but I'll try:

Thank you, heroes
You were angels sent to heal me
and I'll think of you
everyday
for the rest of
my
life

What a beautiful gift
to give someone else
many
more

~~Days~~
~~Years~~
Decades

Surgery Consent

These are the risks:
Seizures
Strokes
Partial paralysis
Paralysis
Cognitive impairment
Death

You might wake up different,
but
you
will
heal

And what if I don't?
My new body is mine too
I will love it
just the same

Why are we talking
about ableism?
When I am
being given
the chance to
survive

Bolt

"This too
shall pass"

And if it doesn't—
I'll learn
to smile
in
the
storm

Lightning bolts
like
rays
of
resilience

4:04

People start to
Look at you differently
when they realize how fragile
your life might be

They don't want to call
because they don't want
to overwhelm you . . .
They mostly don't know what to do

I called my friend from the ER
and she has called me
    every
    day
    since

At the exact same time—
 We laugh
  We cry
   We talk
    We dream

She might not know
that 4:04
saved my life

I will be there
at 4:04
For anyone
that needs me

Mentor

Her story
gave me
permission

To soar
when I felt
like
falling

Patience

I have a visible scar
and it's amazing
how it healed
so quickly
so fiercely

But we can't forget
the internal scars
Those take more time
more heart
more hurt

But they will
heal
again
as well

Try Me

You thought
you could

    Knock
  Me
  Down

Maybe
you couldn't see
the wings
of my community

    Lifting
      Me
        Up

Exist

You don't
have
to suffer
to inspire
others

Your
existence
is
stunning

Disabled

When others say
disabled
They are cautious
I wonder what
they are scared of

When I say
disabled
I am proud
I wonder if
that makes others
proud too

Call me what I am
say it out loud
because
what you are scared of,
I wear as a
badge of honor

Survivors

I look at myself in the mirror
You survived
-and that is enough-
It will *always* be enough

Don't forget
to remind others
that they are
Survivors
too

-We
-Are
-All
-Survivors

Angels

I believe
in people
watching
over me

My angels—
My team—
that help
guide me
through life

I talk
to them
often

I ask for signs
and they
talk back to me

When I feel
alone
I call on
my angels

Angels . . .
I can't do this
alone

Guide me
Protect me
Help me feel you

Therapy

The most
powerful thing
I've learned
in therapy
is to focus
on truths—
on what I know
is fact

I don't know:
What my life will be like in
 Five years
  Ten years
   Twenty . . .

I do know:
 I am strong
  I am resilient
   I can rise again
    I have a community behind me

So, when bad news comes
in tidal waves
I can repeat my truths
to get me
through the hurricane

What is true about you?

Listen

When I was ten,
I learned how to
divide fractions

This year,
I learned how
to listen
to what

my
body
needs

One Day

How do you keep going?

When
 every
  single
 day
hurts

One minute
One day
One week

~at a time~

Brave

It is my hope
that
most people
never
have
to
realize
how
strong
they
really
are

Siblings

My parents
gave me a gift
so big
I unwrap it
over *years*
instead of
minutes

Saudade

I'm not going to miss
the pain
I'm going to miss
what it taught me

I'm not going to miss
the sleepless nights
I'm going to miss
the friendly faces

I'm not going to miss
the tears
I'm going to miss
the people that wiped
them away

I'm not going to miss
the scary thoughts
I'm going to miss
the miracle moments

I'm not going to miss
cold waiting rooms
I'm going to miss
the superwomen
I met in those spaces

I'm not going to miss
the IVs and blood draws
I'm going to miss
the nurse who told me
It's okay to not be okay

I'm not going to miss
the phone call
I'm going to miss
that first beautiful moment
that I felt more
brave than scared

I'm not going to miss
the pain
I'm going to miss
what it taught me

Affirmations

I repeat these
over and
over and
over

When I can't sleep
When the pain is intolerable
When I start questioning

-I feel good
-I feel healthy
-I feel like me
-My body is smart
-My body is healing
-I believe in miracles
-I know miracles are
    on
    their
    way

Strong

I know
I'm strong

I learned that
early on

But
I didn't
want
to
test
it out
this hard

Warriors

Warriors
cry
too

We actually
cry more
when we trade our
swords for words

Showing the world
the river of our
feelings
takes
vulnerability
and
a *different*
kind
of
strength

Scans

You don't
need to be
recovered
from trauma
to be whole

You
were
born
complete

Remission

How will I
live without
the word
remission—
A certificate
that others
hold

Just because things
aren't getting better
It doesn't mean
that they are
getting worse

Stability is a
privilege
that I can live with

Happily
  Fiercely
    Proudly

For the rest of my life

You don't have
to compromise peace
for suspicion

Purpose

Everything is
a gift

The happiness
The good news
The smiles

But what can
be hard
to recognize
are the other gifts

The sorrow
The heartbreak
The seemingly impossible
The devastating
The crushing
The tears

But
I promise,
those are gifts too

They mold you
They shape you

And more than
anything
they give you a
purpose
you would have
otherwise
never known

Take the gifts
life gives you

It is not your job
to understand

It is now your job
to figure out
how to use them

Trust

Sometimes
the only
words that
escape my mouth
the entire day
are

I

Trust

My

Body

Over and over
I regain trust
in a body
that never
misled me
in the first
place

Volume One

Maybe it was
self-assured
to name
this
book
the *first*
volume

The first
implies
a second

—maybe even
a third—

But I can't think
of any other way
I'd rather
live

Knowing that this
is the first
of many,
many, many
more

V1

Acknowledgments

There are so many people who I need to thank for this work. First and foremost, I want to thank all my students who have inspired me throughout my journey as an educator thus far. Teaching you has been the greatest joy in my life and has given me purpose and meaning. Every one of you has taught me something, has made me smile, and given me strength. I wish you all the best.

I'd like to thank my family in the United States and Brazil, my caring parents, my loving siblings, and my very supportive husband. You will never know how much I love you. I'd also like to thank my dog—dogs are the true heroes (Why are there not many people who thank their dogs when they are writing?).

I'd like to thank my mentors—the people who have taught me everything I know: Dr. Elizabeth Buvinger, the educator I strive to be; Dr. Shanna Kattari, who showed me how art could be research; Dr. Mari Kira, a light in this world; and Dr. Nansook Park, the first person to see the teacher in me.

I'd like to thank the medical professionals who have allowed me to be here writing this:

◊ My neurologist—who ordered my MRI and took my concerns seriously.

◊ My neurosurgeon—who gave me the best chance with an incredible surgery and made me feel brave in a time when my world was on fire.

◊ My radiation oncologist—who answered every single one of my questions (there were a lot) and filled me with hope when I needed it most.

◊ My neuro-oncologist—an absolute rock star, badass woman in medicine and my life partner in navigating chronic illness.

◊ Every single nurse, technician, therapist, and administrator—the people that made me feel comfortable and supported.

I will never run out of gratitude for every single person who was there for me in the hospital. Without each one of you, sharing these stories wouldn't be possible.

Lastly, to the reader, teachers, neurodivergent individuals, brain tumor patients, and caregivers, thank you for being brave and doing amazing work. Accessibility is a right, and you deserve the space you have. Keep taking it and showing them what we are made of.

Kiss your big, beautiful brain.

V1

**Thank You, Thank You,
Thank You
from the bottom of my brain**

About the Author

Christina Costa is an academic who teaches psychology to undergraduate and high school students and studies well-being and resilience. She is passionate about inclusive education and also works as a teaching consultant. In 2020, she was diagnosed with a brain tumor (anaplastic astrocytoma) in the right hemisphere of her brain.

As a neurodivergent educator, she hopes to inspire others to celebrate neurodiversity and give hope to other brain cancer and brain tumor patients. Her ultimate goal is to help contribute to the advancement of the science and medicine of brain tumors.

Instagram: @ms.christinacosta

Website: www.christinacosta.net

E-mail: naegeli@umich.edu

125

V1

visit www.teespring.com/stores/kiss-your-brain for brain gear (all proceeds go to brain tumor research)

V1

If you enjoyed *Kiss Your Brain Diagnosis Diaries,* please help others who might enjoy and help raise funds for brain tumor research by leaving a review on amazon.com

Made in the USA
Monee, IL
02 July 2021

72823202R00075